Elefantasy

2022 Calendar

Published by Sellers Publishing, Inc., South Portland, Maine
Calendar © 2021 Sellers Publishing, Inc.
Artwork © 2022 NobleWorks
Licensed by Looking Good Licensing

Astronomical information is in Eastern Time and Daylight Saving Time.
Key to abbreviations: United States (US), Canada (CAN), United Kingdom (UK), Australia (AUS), South Australia (SA),
Western Australia (W. Australia), New South Wales (NSW), Australian Capital Territory (ACT), New Zealand (NZ).

January

May your passion & courage glide you through life.

Sunday	Monday	Tuesday	Wednesday	Thursday	Friday	Saturday
DECEMBER 2021 S M T W T F S 　　　1 2 3 4 5 6 7 8 9 10 11 12 13 14 15 16 17 18 19 20 21 22 23 24 25 26 27 28 29 30 31	**FEBRUARY** S M T W T F S 　　1 2 3 4 5 6 7 8 9 10 11 12 13 14 15 16 17 18 19 20 21 22 23 24 25 26 27 28	28	29	30	31	1 New Year's Day
● NEW MOON 2	3	4	5	6	7	8
9	10	11	12	13	14	15 Martin Luther King Jr.'s Birthday
16	17 Martin Luther King Jr.'s Birthday (observed) ○ FULL MOON	18	19	20	21	22
23/30	24/31	25	26 ● Australia Day	27	28	29

Spread love.

February

Sunday	Monday	Tuesday	Wednesday	Thursday	Friday	Saturday
		Chinese New Year ● NEW MOON	Groundhog Day			
30	**31**	**1**	**2**	**3**	**4**	**5**
Waitangi Day (New Zealand)	Waitangi Day (observed) (New Zealand)					Lincoln's Birthday
6	**7**	**8**	**9**	**10**	**11**	**12**
	Valentine's Day		○ FULL MOON			
13	**14**	**15**	**16**	**17**	**18**	**19**
	Presidents' Day	Washington's Birthday				
20	**21**	**22**	**23**	**24**	**25**	**26**
27	**28**	**1**	**2** ●	**3**		

JANUARY
S	M	T	W	T	F	S
						1
2	3	4	5	6	7	8
9	10	11	12	13	14	15
16	17	18	19	20	21	22
23	24	25	26	27	28	29
30	31					

MARCH
S	M	T	W	T	F	S
		1	2	3	4	5
6	7	8	9	10	11	12
13	14	15	16	17	18	19
20	21	22	23	24	25	26
27	28	29	30	31		

The universe loves a believer.

March

Sunday	Monday	Tuesday	Wednesday	Thursday	Friday	Saturday
			Ash Wednesday ● NEW MOON			
27	28	1	2	3	4	5
	Labour Day (W. Australia)	International Women's Day				
6	7	8	9	10	11	12
Daylight Saving begins	Commonwealth Day (CAN, UK, Australia) Canberra Day (ACT) Labour Day (Victoria)			St. Patrick's Day	○ FULL MOON	
13	14	15	16	17	18	19
Vernal Equinox						
20	21	22	23	24	25	26
Mother's Day (UK)						
27	28	29	30 ●	31		

FEBRUARY
S	M	T	W	T	F	S
		1	2	3	4	5
6	7	8	9	10	11	12
13	14	15	16	17	18	19
20	21	22	23	24	25	26
27	28					

APRIL
S	M	T	W	T	F	S
					1	2
3	4	5	6	7	8	9
10	11	12	13	14	15	16
17	18	19	20	21	22	23
24	25	26	27	28	29	30

Life is an adventure, roll with it.

April

Sunday	Monday	Tuesday	Wednesday	Thursday	Friday	Saturday
MARCH S M T W T F S 1 2 3 4 5 6 7 8 9 10 11 12 13 14 15 16 17 18 19 20 21 22 23 24 25 26 27 28 29 30 31	**MAY** S M T W T F S 1 2 3 4 5 6 7 8 9 10 11 12 13 14 15 16 17 18 19 20 21 22 23 24 25 26 27 28 29 30 31	**29**	**30**	**31**	● NEW MOON **1**	**2**
3 Palm Sunday	**4**	**5**	**6**	**7**	**8** Good Friday Passover begins at sundown	**9** ○ FULL MOON
10 Easter Sunday	**11** Easter Monday (CAN, UK, AUS, NZ)	**12**	**13**	**14**	**15** Earth Day	**16**
17	**18**	**19**	**20**	**21**	**22**	**23**
24	**25** ANZAC Day (Australia, NZ)	**26**	**27** ● Holocaust Remembrance Day begins at sundown	**28**	**29** Arbor Day	**30** ● NEW MOON

Happiness is a treasure meant to be shared.

May

Sunday	Monday	Tuesday	Wednesday	Thursday	Friday	Saturday
May Day	Bank Holiday (UK) Labour Day (Queensland)					
1	**2**	**3**	**4**	**5**	**6**	**7**
Mother's Day (US, CAN, AUS, NZ)						
8	**9**	**10**	**11**	**12**	**13**	**14**
	○ FULL MOON					Armed Forces Day
15	**16**	**17**	**18**	**19**	**20**	**21**
	Victoria Day (Canada)					
22	**23**	**24**	**25**	**26**	**27**	**28**
	Memorial Day ● NEW MOON					
29	**30**	**31**	1 ●	2		

APRIL

S	M	T	W	T	F	S
					1	2
3	4	5	6	7	8	9
10	11	12	13	14	15	16
17	18	19	20	21	22	23
24	25	26	27	28	29	30

JUNE

S	M	T	W	T	F	S
			1	2	3	4
5	6	7	8	9	10	11
12	13	14	15	16	17	18
19	20	21	22	23	24	25
26	27	28	29	30		

Be on the lookout for adventure.

June

Sunday	Monday	Tuesday	Wednesday	Thursday	Friday	Saturday
MAY S M T W T F S 1 2 3 4 5 6 7 8 9 10 11 12 13 14 15 16 17 18 19 20 21 22 23 24 25 26 27 28 29 30 31	JULY S M T W T F S 1 2 3 4 5 6 7 8 9 10 11 12 13 14 15 16 17 18 19 20 21 22 23 24 25 26 27 28 29 30 31	**31**	**1**	Bank Holiday (UK) **2**	Platinum Jubilee Bank Holiday (UK) **3**	**4**
5	Queen's Birthday (New Zealand) **6**	**7**	**8**	**9**	**10**	**11**
12	Queen's Birthday (Australia) **13**	Flag Day ○ FULL MOON **14**	**15**	**16**	**17**	**18**
Father's Day (US, Canada, UK) Juneteenth **19**	**20**	Summer Solstice **21**	**22**	**23**	**24**	**25**
26	**27**	● NEW MOON **28**	**29** ●	**30**	**1**	**2**

There are no maps to the best places — follow your heart.

Sunday	Monday	Tuesday	Wednesday	Thursday	Friday	Saturday
JUNE S M T W T F S 1 2 3 4 5 6 7 8 9 10 11 12 13 14 15 16 17 18 19 20 21 22 23 24 25 26 27 28 29 30	AUGUST S M T W T F S 1 2 3 4 5 6 7 8 9 10 11 12 13 14 15 16 17 18 19 20 21 22 23 24 25 26 27 28 29 30 31	28	29	30	**Canada Day** 1	2
3	**Independence Day** 4	5	6	7	8	9
10	11	12	○ FULL MOON 13	14	15	16
17	18	19	20	21	22	23
24/31	25	26	● NEW MOON 27 ●	28	29	30

Be amazing — you never know who you're inspiring.

Sunday	Monday	Tuesday	Wednesday	Thursday	Friday	Saturday
31	1 Civic Holiday (Canada) Bank Holiday (NSW)	2	3	4 ○ FULL MOON	5	6
7	8	9	10	11	12	13
14	15	16	17	18	19	20 ● NEW MOON
21	22	23	24	25	26	27
28	29 Bank Holiday (UK)	30	31 ●	1		

JULY
S	M	T	W	T	F	S
					1	2
3	4	5	6	7	8	9
10	11	12	13	14	15	16
17	18	19	20	21	22	23
24	25	26	27	28	29	30
31						

SEPTEMBER
S	M	T	W	T	F	S
				1	2	3
4	5	6	7	8	9	10
11	12	13	14	15	16	17
18	19	20	21	22	23	24
25	26	27	28	29	30	

It only seems impossible until you do it.

September

Sunday	Monday	Tuesday	Wednesday	Thursday	Friday	Saturday
AUGUST S M T W T F S 1 2 3 4 5 6 7 8 9 10 11 12 13 14 15 16 17 18 19 20 21 22 23 24 25 26 27 28 29 30 31	OCTOBER S M T W T F S 1 2 3 4 5 6 7 8 9 10 11 12 13 14 15 16 17 18 19 20 21 22 23 24 25 26 27 28 29 30 31	**30**	**31**	**1**	**2**	**3**
Father's Day (Australia, NZ) **4**	Labor Day (US, Canada) **5**	**6**	**7**	**8**	**9**	○ FULL MOON **10**
Patriot Day **11**	**12**	**13**	**14**	**15**	**16**	**17**
18	**19**	**20**	UN International Day of Peace **21**	Autumnal Equinox **22**	**23**	**24**
Rosh Hashanah begins at sundown ● NEW MOON **25**	Queen's Birthday (W. Australia) **26**	**27**	**28** ●	**29**	**30**	**1**

Carve out some time for the good things in life.

October

Sunday	Monday	Tuesday	Wednesday	Thursday	Friday	Saturday

SEPTEMBER
S M T W T F S
1 2 3
4 5 6 7 8 9 10
11 12 13 14 15 16 17
18 19 20 21 22 23 24
25 26 27 28 29 30

NOVEMBER
S M T W T F S
1 2 3 4 5
6 7 8 9 10 11 12
13 14 15 16 17 18 19
20 21 22 23 24 25 26
27 28 29 30

Sunday	Monday	Tuesday	Wednesday	Thursday	Friday	Saturday
		27	28	29	30	1
2	Labour Day (ACT, NSW, SA) / Queen's Birthday (Queensland) **3**	Yom Kippur begins at sundown **4**	5	6	7	8
○ FULL MOON **9**	Columbus Day (observed) / Thanksgiving (Canada) / Indigenous Peoples' Day (observed) **10**	11	12	13	14	15
16	17	18	19	20	21	22
23/30	Labour Day (24th) (New Zealand) / Halloween (31st) **24/31**	● NEW MOON **25**	26 ●	27	28	29

Let your imagination soar and take flight.

November

Sunday	Monday	Tuesday	Wednesday	Thursday	Friday	Saturday
		All Saints' Day				
30	31	1	2	3	4	5
Daylight Saving ends		Election Day ○ FULL MOON			Veterans Day Remembrance Day (CAN, AUS, NZ)	
6	7	8	9	10	11	12
Remembrance Sunday (UK)						
13	14	15	16	17	18	19
			● NEW MOON	Thanksgiving		
20	21	22	23	24	25	26
					OCTOBER	DECEMBER
27	28	29	30 ●	1		

OCTOBER
S M T W T F S
                1
2 3 4 5 6 7 8
9 10 11 12 13 14 15
16 17 18 19 20 21 22
23 24 25 26 27 28 29
30 31

DECEMBER
S M T W T F S
          1 2 3
4 5 6 7 8 9 10
11 12 13 14 15 16 17
18 19 20 21 22 23 24
25 26 27 28 29 30 31